POOR PUPPY

BY Nick Bruel

SCHOLASTIC INC.

New York   Toronto   London   Auckland   Sydney
Mexico City   New Delhi   Hong Kong   Buenos Aires

Puppy's best friend is Kitty.

But Puppy
is sad.

**Kitty doesn't
want to play
with him
today.**

Poor Puppy.

Poor, poor Puppy.

Poor, poor, poor, poor,
POOR
Puppy!

Instead of Kitty, the only things Puppy has to play with are . . .

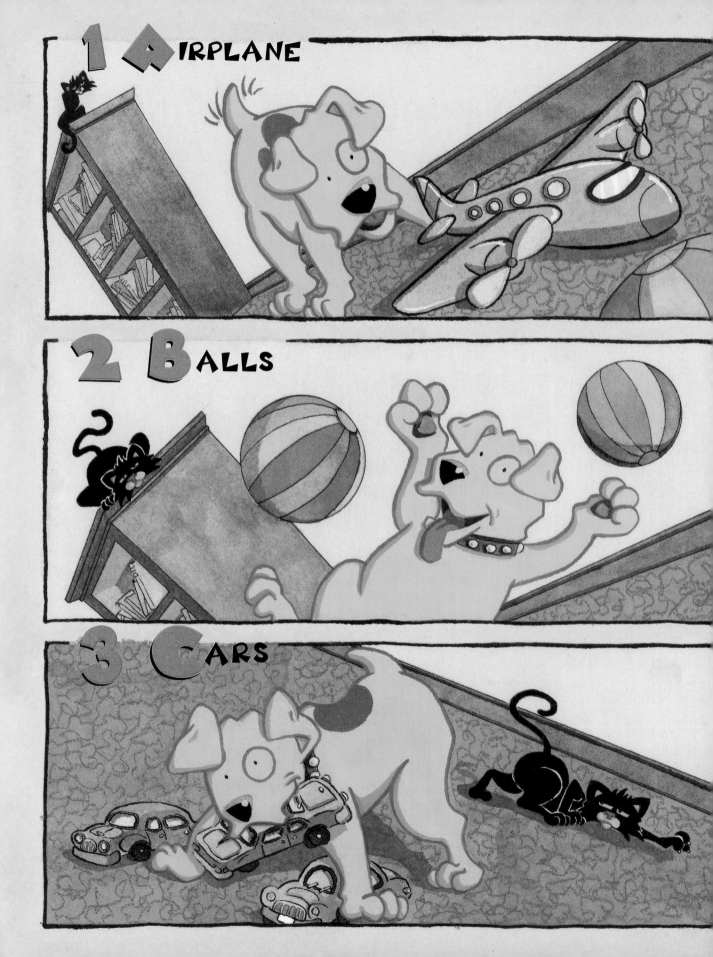

4 **D**OLLS

5 **E**LECTRIC TRAINS

6 **F**INGER PUPPETS

9 **I**NSTRUMENTS

10 JACKS

11 Kites

12 Liters of Fingerpaints

17 Queens, Kings, Knights, Bishops, Castles and Pawns

18 Robots

21 Ukuleles

22 Valentines

23 WIND-UP TOYS

24 BOXES OF CRAYONS

That was FUN!
But Puppy really wanted to
play with Kitty.

Poor Puppy.

Now he's so tired,
he has to take a nap.

Poor Puppy.

When Puppy naps, he dreams.

What do you think he dreams about?

He dreams about playing with Kitty, of course!

They play . . .

. . . Puppy wakes up.

What a great dream!
Now Puppy is so happy,
he wants to play!

And so does Kitty!

HOORAY!